VOLUME IV.

ALBUM

OF

TYNESIDE SONGS

WITH ACCOMPANIMENTS

BY

SAMUEL REAY, Mus. Bac.

PUBLISHED BY

J. G. WINDOWS Ltd.,

Piano & Music Warehouse,

Central Arcade, Newcastle-on-Tyne

(COPYRIGHT)

SAIR FYEL'D, HINNY

Moderato. About ♩ = 76.

Sair fyel'd, hin-ny, Sair fyel'd now; Sair fyel'd, hin-ny, Sin' aw ken'd thou.

Aw was young and lus-ty, Aw was fair and clear; Aw was young and lus-ty, Mony a lang year.

SAIR fyel'd, hinny,
    Sair fyel'd now;
Sair fyel'd, hinny,
    Sin' I ken'd thou.
Aw was young and lusty,
    Aw was fair and clear;
Aw was young and lusty
    Mony a lang year.
        Sair fyel'd, hinny, etc.

When aw was young and lusty
    Aw cou'd lowp a dyke;
But now aw'm awd an' stiff
    Aw can hardly step a syke.
        Sair fyel'd, hinny, etc.

When aw was five-and-twenty
    Aw was brave and bauld;
Now, at five-and-sixty,
    Aw'm byeth stiff and cauld.
        Sair fyel'd, hinny, etc.

Thus said the auld man
    To the oak tree:
"Sair fyel'd is aw
    Sin' aw ken'd thee."
        Sair fyel'd, hinny, etc.

NEWCASTLE IS MY NATIVE PLACE.

New - cas - tle is my native place, Where my mother sigh'd for

me; I was born in New - cas - tle Chare, The cen - tre of the Kee; Where in

ear - ly youth I sport - ed, Quite free from care and pain! But a - las! those days are

past and gone, They'll nev - er come a - gain. No, they'll nev - er come a - gain, They'll

nev - er come a - gain; A - las! those days are past and gone, They'll nev - er come a - gain.

NEWCASSEL is my native place,
　Where my mother sighed for me,
I was born in Rewcastle Chare,
　The centre of the Kee;
Where in early youth I sported,
　Quite free from care and pain!
But, alas! those days are gone and past,
　They'll never come again.

They sent me to the Jub'lee school
　A scholar to make me,
Where Tommy Penn, my monitor,
　Learnt me my A, B, C;
My master to correct me then
　He often used the cane,
But I can say with confidence
　He'll never do't again.

Now like another youth I had
　A love to grace my side,
I often whispered in her ear
　That she should be my bride;
And when I kissed her rosy lips,
　She cried "O fie, for shame!"
But with "Good-night," she always said,
　"O, mind come back again!"

At length I had to go to trade,—
　I went to serve my time;
The world with all its flattering charms
　Before me seemed to shine;
When plenty cash was in my store,
　I never did complain,
Alas! those days are gone and past,
　They'll never come again.

At length to church I gladly went
　With Nancy to be wed,
The thought of martimony came
　And troubled then my head;
The priest that tied the fatal knot,
　I now could tell him plain
That, if I was once more single,
　He should never tie't again.

Now like another married man,
　I have with care to fight,
So let all joy and happiness
　Among us reign to-night;
And with a bumper in each hand,
　Let every heart proclaim,
That happy may we separate,
　And happy meet again.

BOBBY SHAFTOE.

Bob-by Shaf-toe's gaen to sea, Sil-ver buck-les at his knee; He'll come back and

mar-ry me, Bon-ny Bob-by Shaf-toe. Bob-by Shaftoe's bright and fair, Combing down his

yel-low hair; He's my awn for ev-er-mair, Bon-ny Bob-by Shaf-toe.

BOBBY SHAFTOE.

BOBBY SHAFTOE'S gaen to sea,
Siller buckles on his knee,
He'll come back and marry me,
    Bonny Bobby Shaftoe.
Bobby Shaftoe's bright and fair,
Combing down his yellow hair;
He's me awn for iver mair,
    Bonny Bobby Shaftoe.

Bobby Shaftoe hes a bairn
For to dangle on his airm;
In his airm and on his knee,
    Bonny Bobby Shaftoe.
Bobby Shaftoe's gaen to sea,
Siller buckles on his knee,
He'll come back and marry me,
    Bonny Bobby Shaftoe.

THE WATER OF TYNE.

Andante con moto. About ♪ = 120.

I cannot get to my love if I would dee, The water of Tyne runs be-tween him and me; And here I must stand, with the tear in my e'e, Both sigh-ing and sick-ly my sweet-heart to see.

THE WATER OF TYNE.

I CANNOT get to my love, if I would dee,
  The water of Tyne runs between him and me;
And here I must stand with the tear in my e'e,
  Both sighing and sickly my sweetheart to see.

O where is the boatman? my bonny hinny!
  O where is the boatman? bring him to me,—
To ferry me over the Tyne to my honey,
  And I will remember the boatman and thee.

O bring me a boatman, I'll give any money,
  And you for your trouble rewarded shall be,—
To ferry me over the Tyne to my honey,
  Or scull him across that rough river to me.

O THE OAK, AND THE ASH, AND THE BONNY IVY TREE.

A North Countrie lass up to Lon-don did pass, Although with her na - ture it did not a-gree, Which

made her re-pent and so oft - en la-ment, Still wish-ing a - gain in the North for to be. O the

oak, and the ash, and the bon-ny i - vy tree, Do flour - ish at home in the North Coun - trie.

O THE OAK, AND THE ASH, AND THE BONNY IVY TREE.

A NORTH-COUNTRY lass up to London did pass,
  Although with her nature it did not agree,
Which made her repent and so often lament,
  Still wishing again in the North for to be.
    O the oak, and the ash, and the bonny ivy tree
    Do flourish at home in my own countrie.

Fain would I be in the North Country,
  Where the lads and the lasses are making of hay;
There should I see what is pleasant to me,
  A mischief light on them enticed me away.
    O the oak, and the ash, and the bonny ivy tree
    Do flourish most bravely in our countrie.

Since that I came forth of the pleasant North
  There's nothing delightful I see doth abound;
They never can be half so merry as we,
  When we are a-dancing of Sellinger's Round.
    O the oak, and the ash, and the bonny ivy tree
    Do flourish at home in our own countrie.

I like not the court, nor to city resort,
  Since there is no fancy for such maids as me;
Their pomp and their pride I can never abide
  Because with my humour it doth not agree.
    O the oak, and the ash, and the bonny ivy tree
    Do flourish at home in my own countrie.

How oft have I been on the Westmoreland Green,
  Where the young men and maidens resort for to
    play;
Where we with delight, from morning till night,
  Could feast it and frolic on each holiday.
    O the oak, and the ash, and the bonny ivy tree
    Do flourish most bravely in our countrie.

A-milking to go, all the maids in a row,
  It was a fine sight, and pleasant to see;
But here in the city they're void of all pity—
  There is no enjoyment of liberty.
    O the oak, and the ash, and the bonny ivy tree,
    They flourish most bravely in our countrie.

When I had the heart from my friends to depart,
  I thought I should be a lady at last;
But now do I find that it troubles my mind
  Because that my joys and my pleasures are past.
    O the oak, and the ash, and the bonny ivy tree,
    They flourish at home in my own countrie.

The ewes and the lambs, with the kids and their
    dams,
  To see in the country how finely they play;
The bells they do ring, and the birds they do sing,
  And the fields and the gardens so pleasant and gay
    O the oak, and the ash, and the bonny ivy tree,
    They flourish at home in my own countrie.

At wakes and at fairs, being 'void of all cares,
  We there with our lovers did used for to dance;
Then hard hap had I, my ill fortune to try,
  And so up to London my steps to advance.
    O the oak, and the ash, and the bonny ivy tree,
    They flourish most bravely in our countrie.

But still I perceive I a husband might have,
  If I to the city my mind could but frame;
But I'll have a lad that is North-Country bred,
  Or else I'll not marry, in the mind that I am.
    O the oak, and the ash, and the bonny ivy tree,
    They flourish most bravely in our countrie.

A maiden I am, and a maid I'll remain,
  Until my own country again I do see;
For here in this place I shall ne'er see the face
  Of him that's allotted my love for to be.
    O the oak, and the ash, and the bonny ivy tree,
    They flourish at home in my own countrie.

Then farewell, my daddy, and farewell, my mammy,
  Until I do see you I nothing but mourn;
Rememb'ring my brothers, my sisters, and others,
  In less than a year I hope to return.
    Then the oak, and the ash, and the bonny ivy tree,
    I shall see them at home in my own countrie.

OH! I HA'E SEEN THE ROSES BLAW.

Oh! I ha'e seen the ro-ses blaw, The heather bloom, the broom and a' The li-ly spring as white as snaw, With all their na-tive splen-dour; Yet Ma-ry's sweet-er, on the green As fresh and fair as Flora's queen; Mair stately than the branching bean, Or like the i-vy slen-der.

OH! I HA'E SEEN THE ROSES BLAW.

OH! I ha'e seen the roses blaw,
The heather bloom, the broom and a',
The lily spring as white as snaw,
    With all their native splendour.
Yet Mary's sweeter on the green,
As fresh and fair as Flora's queen,
Mair stately than the branching bean,
    Or like the ivy slender.

In nature, like a summer day,
Transcendent as a sunny ray,
Her shape and air is frank and gay,
    With all that's sweet and tender.
While lav'rocks sing their cheerful lays,
And shepherds brush the dewy braes,
To meet wi' Mary's bonny face,
    Among the shades I wander.

My captive breast, by fancy led,
Adores the sweet, the lovely maid,
Wi' ilka smile and charm arrayed,
    To make a heart surrender.
I love her mair than bees do flowers,
Or birds the pleasant leafy bowers,
Her presence yields me what the showers
    To hills and valleys render.

Could I obtain my charmer's love,
Mair stable than a rock I'd prove,
With all the meekness of a dove,
    To ilka pleasure hand her.
If she would like a shepherd lad,
I'd change my cane, my crook, and plaid,
Upon the hill tune up a reed,
    And with a song commend her.

For her I'd lead a life remote,
Wi' her I'd love a rustic cot,
There bless kind fortune for my lot,
    And ilka comfort lend her.
Till death seals up my wearied e'e,
In troubled dreams her form I'll see;
Till she consents to live with me,
    In lonesome shades I'll wander.

ELSIE MARLEY.

Di' ye ken El - sie Mar - ley, ho- ney? The wife that sells the bar - ley, ho- ney; She

lost her pock-et and all her mon-ey, A - back o' the bush i' the gar - den, hon - ey.

El - sie Mar - ley's grown so fine, She won't get up to serve the swine, But

ELSIE MARLEY—continued.

lies in bed till eight or nine, And sure-ly she does take her time.

Di' ye ken Elsie Marley, honey?
The wife that sells the barley, honey;
She lost her pocket and all her money,
Aback o' the bush i' the garden, honey.

Elsie Marley's grown so fine,
She won't get up to serve the swine,
But lies in bed till eight or nine,
And surely she does take her time.
     Di' ye ken Elsie Marley? etc.

Elsie Marley is so neat,
It's hard for one to walk the street,
But every lad and lass they meet
Cries "Di' ye ken Elsie Marley, honey?"
     Di' ye ken Elsie Marley? etc.

Elsie Marley wore a straw hat,
But now she's getten a velvet cap;
The Lambton lads mun pay for that,
Di' ye ken Elsie Marley, honey?
     Di' ye ken Elsie Marley? etc.

Elsie keeps rum, gin, and ale,
In her house below the dale,
Where every tradesman, up and down,
Does call and spend his half-a-crown.
     Di' ye ken Elsie Marley? etc.

The farmers, as they cum that way,
They drink with Elsie every day,
And call the fiddler for to play
The tune of "Elsie Marley," honey.
     Di' ye ken Elsie Marley? etc.

The pitmen and the keelmen trim
They drink Bumbo made of gin,
And for to dance they do begin
To the tune of "Elsie Marley," honey.
     Di' ye ken Elsie Marley? etc.

The sailors they do call for flip,
As soon as they come from the ship,
And then begin to dance and skip
To the tune of "Elsie Marley," honey.
     Di' ye ken Elsie Marley? etc.

Those gentlemen that go so fine,
They'll treat her with a bottle of wine,
And freely they'll sit down and dine
Along with Elsie Marley, honey.
     Di' ye ken Elsie Marley? etc.

So to conclude those lines I've penn'd,
Hoping there's none I do offend,
And thus my merry joke doth end
Concerning Elsie Marley, honey.
     Di' ye ken Elsie Marley? etc.

DANCE TI' THY DADDY.

Brightly. *About* ♩ = 108.

Come here, maw lit-tle Jack-y, Now aw've smok'd mi backy, Let's hev a bit o' cracky, Till the boat comes in.

Dance ti' thy dad-dy, Sing ti' thy mammy, Dance ti' thy dad-dy, Ti' thy mammy sing.

Thou shall hev a fish-y On a lit-tle dish-y, Thou shall hev a fish-y When the boat comes in.

DANCE TI' THY DADDY.

COME here, maw little Jacky,
Now aw've smok'd mi backy,
Let's hev a bit o' cracky,
Till the boat comes in.

Dance ti' thy daddy, sing ti' thy mammy,
Dance ti' thy daddy, ti' thy mammy sing;
Thou shall hev a fishy on a little dishy,
Thou shall hev a fishy when the boat comes in.

Here's thy mother humming,
Like a canny woman;
Yonder comes thy father,
Drunk—he cannot stand.

Dance ti' thy daddy, sing ti' thy mammy,
Dance ti' thy daddy, ti' thy mammy sing;
Thou shall hev a fishy on a little dishy,
Thou shall hev a haddock when the boat comes in.

Our Tommy's always fuddling,
He's so fond of ale,
But he's kind to me,
I hope he'll never fail.

Dance ti' thy daddy, sing ti' thy mammy,
Dance ti' thy daddy, ti' thy mammy sing;
Thou shall hev a fishy on a little dishy,
Thou shall hev a bloater when the boat comes in.

I like a drop mysel',
When I can get it sly,
And thou, my bonny bairn,
Will lik't as weil as I.

Dance ti' thy daddy, sing ti' thy mammy,
Dance ti' thy daddy, ti' thy mammy sing;
Thou shall hev a fishy on a little dishy,
Thou shall hev a mackerel when the boat comes in.

May we get a drop,
Oft as we stand in need;
And weel may the keel row
That brings the bairns their bread.

Dance ti' thy daddy, sing ti' thy mammy,
Dance ti' thy daddy, ti' thy mammy sing;
Thou shall hev a fishy on a little dishy,
Thou shall hev a salmon when the boat comes in.

THE FIERY CLOCK FYECE.

Lively. ♩. = 96.

O Dick, what's kept ye a' this time? Aw've fretted sair a - boot ye; Aw thought that ye'd fa'n in the Tyne, Then what wad aw deun with - oot ye? O hin- ny, Dol- ly, sit thee doon, And hear the news aw've brought fra toon, The New-cas- sel folks hes catch'd a moon, And myed it a bon - ny clock fyece.

THE FIERY CLOCK-FYECE.

O DICK, what's kept ye a' this time?
  Aw've fretted sair aboot ye;
Aw thowt that ye'd fa'n in the Tyne,
  Then what wad aw deun withoot ye?
O hinny, Dolly, sit thee doon,
And hear the news aw've browt fra toon—
The Newcassel folks hes catch'd a moon,
  An' myed it a bonny clock-fyece.

Thou knaws St. Nicholas' Church, maw pet,
  Where we war tied together—
That place, aw knaw, thou'll not forget,
  Forget it aw will niver.
'Twas there then, jewel, aw saw the seet,
As aw cam staggerin' through the street—
Aw thowt it queer at pick-dark neet
  Te see a fiery clock-fyece.

The folks they stood in flocks aboot—
  Aw cried, "How! what's the matter?"
Aw glowered—at last aw gov a shoot
  For them te fetch sum watter;
The church is afire, and varry suin
That bonny place 'ill be burnt doon—
Ye fyul, says a chep, it's a bonny moon
  They've catched an' myed it a clock-fyece.

On Monday, when aw gan te wark,
  Aw'll surely tell wor banksman,
If we had sic a leet at dark,
  We niver wad break wor shanks, man;
Maw marrows an' aw'll gan te the toon
Te see if we can catch a moon—
If we can only coax one doon,
  We'll myek't a bonny clock-fyece.

Then if we get it doon the pit,
  We'll hed stuck on a pole, man;
'Twill tell us how wor time gans on,
  Likewise to hew wor coal, man.
So now, maw pet, let's gan te bed,
An' not forget the neet we wed,
The morn we'll tell wor Uncle Ned
  Aboot the bonny clock-fyece.

THE GYETSIDE LASS.

Allegretto. ♩. = 96.

Tune—" All round my hat."

Aw warn'd ye hev - ent seen my lass, her nyem aw win - not men - shun, For fear ye gan an' tell her how aw like her,—so **aw dee**; But just for lads an' lass - es te whis - per their af - fec - shun, The bon - niest lass o' Gyetside's bon - ny fye - ces both - er'd me.

MAW BONNY GYETSIDE LASS!

Aw warn'd ye hevent seen me lass—her nyem aw winnet menshun,
  For fear ye gan an' tell her hoo aw like her, so aw de!
But it's just for lads an' lasses te whispor thor affecshun,
  The bonniest lass o' Gyetside's bonny fyece's brothered me.

The forst time aw saw her, whey aw's sure aw diddint knaw her,
  Tho' aw thowt aw'd seen her fyece afore, but cuddint think o' where;
Her blue eye met mine i' passin' up High Street, i' the mornin',
  An' her luik wes se intransin, that me heart wes mine ne mair.

Aw diddent see her for a week, till one neet at the Bridge End,
  When aw strampt upon her goon, an' the gethors com away;
She said that aw wes clumsy, an' aw said that aw wes sorry,
  An' aw humbly beg'd her pardon,—aw wes lickt for what te say.

But aw wawk'd on biv her side just as if aw had a reet te did,
  The convorsayshun forst wes shy, at last it turn'd forst-class;
We byeth spoke aboot the weather—an' she menshun'd that her fethur
  Wes a puddlor doon at Hawks's—Oh, maw bonny Gyetside Lass!

She menshun'd confidenshly that her unkil wes a grossor,
  An' his muther's fether's cussin wes a fiddler doon the shore;
An' she spoke se nice an' frindly, an' smil'd se sweet an' plissint,
  That aw thowt aw'd nivor seen a lass se charmin' like before.

She said her muthor kept a shop, an' sell'd het pies an' candy,
  An' her bruther wes a cobbler at the high pairt o' the toon;
An' she wes a dressmaker—we got se kind together,
  That aw blis't aw'd been se awkword as aw strampt upon her goon.

Aw myed her laff an' slap me lug, wi' tawkin' lots o' nonsense,
  But, bliss ye, when yor curtin thor's nowt se gud 'ill pass;
Aw askt her wad she be me lass, an' aw'd tyek her oot on Sunday,
  To maw delite, she said aw might, maw bonny Gyetside Lass!

CA' HAWKIE THROUGH THE WATER.

Allegro moderato. ♩ = 108.

mf

cres.

f

mf

mf

Ca' Haw-kie, Ca' Haw-kie, Ca' Haw-kie through the wa-ter. Haw-kie is a

sweir beast, And Haw-kie win-na wade the wa-ter. Haw-kie is a bon-ny cow,

cres.   *f*   *D.C.*

Though she's loth to wade the wa-ter; While she waits the wark'll stand, So ca' Haw-kie through the wa-ter.

cres.   *f*   *D.C.*

CA' HAWKIE THROUGH THE WATER

Ca' Hawkie, ca' Hawkie,
  Ca' Hawkie through the water;
Hawkie is a sweir beast,
  And Hawkie winna wade the water.

Hawkie is a bonny cow,
  Though she's loth to wade the water;
While she waits the wark 'll stand,
  So ca' Hawkie through the water.

Hawkie is a pretty cow;
  All the children do adore her,
For she gives them all the milk—
  There is none they prize before her.

Girls, be not too nice and coy,
  If your sweethearts want to marry,
Ne'er say nay, but quick comply,
  As 'tis hazardous to tarry.

Now, young maids, my counsel take,
  Since that it can be no better;
Cast off baith your hose and shoon,
  And safely drive her through the water.

UP THE RAW.

Up the Raw, Up the Raw, Up the Raw, lass, ev'-ry day,—

For shape and co-lour, ma bon-ny hin-ny, Thou bangs thy mother, ma can-ny bairn.

Black as a craw, maw bon-ny hin-ny, Thou bangs them a', lass, ev'-ry day.

Thou's a' clag can-died, ma bon-ny hinny; Thou's dou-ble ja-pan-ded, ma can-ny bairn.

Up the Raw, down the Raw,
Up the Raw, lass, ev'ry day;
For shape and colour, ma bonny hinny,
Thou bangs thy mother, ma canny bairn.

Black as a craw, ma bonny hinny,
Thou bangs them a', lass, ev'ry day;
Thou's a' clag-candied, ma bonny hinny,
Thou's double japanded, ma canny bairn.
      Up the Raw, etc,

For hide and hue, ma bonny hinny,
Thou bangs the craw, ma canny bairn,
Up the Raw, ma bonny hinny,
Thou bangs them a', ma canny bairn.
      Up the Raw, etc.

DOL-LI-A.

Fresh aw cum frae Sandgate Street — Dol - li, Dol - li, — Maw best friends here to meet — Dol - li - a.

Dol - li the dil - len dol, Dol - li, Dol - li, Dol - li the dil - len dol, Dol - li - a.

DOL-LI-A.

FRESH aw cum frae Sandgate Street,
    Dol-li, dol-li,
Maw best freends here to meet,
    Dol-li-a.
      Dol-li the dillen dol,
        Dol-li, dol-li,
      Dol-li the dillen dol,
        Dol-li-a.

The Black Cuffs is gawn away,
An' that'll be a crying day.

Dolly Coxon's pawned her shirt
To ride upon the baggage-cart.

The Green Cuffs is cummin' in,
An' that'll make the lasses sing.

ABOOT THE BUSH, WILLY.

A - boot the bush, Wil-ly, a - boot the bee-hive, A - boot the bush, Wil-ly, I'll meet thee, be-lyve;

Then to my ten shillings add you but a groat, I'll go to New-cas-tle and buy a new coat.

ABOOT the bush, Willy,
　Aboot the bee-hive,
Aboot the bush, Willy,
　I'll meet thee belyve.

Then to my ten shillings
　Add you but a groat;
I'll go to Newcastle
　And buy a new coat.

Five and five shillings,
　Five and a crown;
Five and five shillings
　Will buy a new gown.

Five and five shillings,
　Five and a groat;
Five and five shillings
　Will buy a new coat.